People can make a difference in their communities.

Copyright acknowledgments and credits appear on page 160, which constitutes an extension of this copyright page.

Copyright © 1996 by Scholastic Inc.   All rights reserved.   Printed in the U.S.A.
ISBN 0-590-49159-8

2 3 4 5 6 7 8 9 10   23   02 01 00 99 98 97 96

POLICE DEPT.

WELCOME to ISLETA PUEBLO
• CHR • SOCIAL SERVICES • WIC • D.V.R.
HOURS - 8:00 A.M. - 4:30 MON. - FRI.

POLICE

Go to
a Police Station

People can make a
difference in their
communities.

A Place in History

We celebrate people who made the world better.

All in a Day's Work

We celebrate people who make their communities better.

Small Ways

The little things we do can make a big difference.

Trade Books

The following books accompany this *Lend a Hand* SourceBook.

Mystery

Cam Jansen and the Mystery of the Babe Ruth Baseball

by David A. Adler
illustrated by Susanna Natti

Fantasy
The Conversation Club
by Diane Stanley

Realistic Fiction
The Car Washing Street

by Denise Lewis Patrick
illustrated by John Ward

Big Book

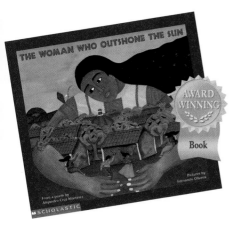

Legend
The Woman Who Outshone the Sun

from a poem by
Alejandro Cruz Martinez
illustrated by Fernando Olivera

7

A Place in History

We celebrate people who made the world better.

Find out some of the amazing things that Benjamin Franklin did.

Learn about slaves who escaped and the many people who helped them along the way.

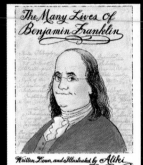
from

The Many Lives of Benjamin Franklin

By Aliki

Benjamin Franklin did so many amazing things that it seems as if he lived many lives. He opened a printing shop and printed his own newspaper. He lent out his many books and started the first free lending library in America. He started a police force, a fire department, and a hospital.

Franklin also invented many useful things. The Franklin stove could heat a whole house. The lightning rod protected houses from lightning. Franklin never took money for any of his inventions. He said his ideas belonged to everyone.

People put "Franklin Rods" upon their rooftops in America and in other countries, too.

Benjamin and his friends discussed ways to gain freedom for America.

More than anything, Benjamin hoped people would
listen to his most important idea—
freedom for his country.
For at that time, America was an English colony.
He—and others—did not want to be ruled by
England any longer.

He was sent to England to seek independence
for his country.
For eighteen long years, Benjamin stayed there
and worked for that goal.
In 1775, he returned to Philadelphia,
sad and disappointed.
His wife had died. War with England had begun,
and America was still not free.

Pennsylvania State House, now called Independence Hall, in 1776.

Benjamin Franklin, Thomas Jefferson, John Adams, John Hancock, and 52 others, signed the Declaration of Independence in Philadelphia on July 4, 1776.

12

Yet he persisted.

Benjamin Franklin and other great Americans
helped Thomas Jefferson write the Declaration of
Independence.

They were determined to be free.

They knew they would have to fight
a long, terrible war.

And fight they did.

General George Washington led many battles during the
Revolutionary War.

In France, he visited King Louis XVI and Queen Marie Antoinette. Though everyone wore fancy clothes and powdered wigs, Benjamin Franklin did not. Everyone was impressed with the inventor's plain clothes and simple ways.

But they needed more help.
Benjamin Franklin was old and weary when again
he sailed away.
This time he went to ask for aid from
the King of France.

Benjamin was greeted as a hero.
People in France knew about him and his inventions,
and they loved him.
Finally, the King agreed.
With his help, the war with England was won.
America was free at last.

In 1781 the war ended. The Liberty Bell in Independence Hall rang out.

On September 13, 1785, his ship entered Philadelphia Harbor. Bells rang, cannons boomed, and hundreds of people waited to welcome Benjamin home.

He was reunited at last with his daughter Sally, her husband Richard Bache, and his grandchildren.

Benjamin Franklin had served abroad long enough.

He wanted to spend his last years at home.

When he finally returned from France, it was 1785.

He thought he had been forgotten.

But he had not been forgotten.

He was greeted with wild celebrations.

He saw his country still needed him.

He became the first governor of Pennsylvania and

helped write the Constitution of the United States.

Benjamin Franklin lived eighty-four years.

He left the world his inventions, his ideas,

his wisdom and his wit.

He lived his many lives for us all.

On September 17, 1787, Benjamin Franklin and the other great writers of the Constitution signed the document on which all laws of the United States are based.

AWARD
WINNING
Book

Follow
THE DRINKING GOURD

STORY AND PICTURES BY JEANETTE WINTER

FOLLOW THE DRINKING GOURD

Long ago,
before the Civil War,
there was an old sailor called Peg Leg Joe
who did what he could to help free the slaves.

Joe had a plan.
He'd use hammer and nail and saw
and work for the master, the man
who owned the slaves
on the cotton plantation.

Joe had a plan.
At night when work was done,
he'd teach the slaves a song
that secretly told the way
to freedom.
Just follow the drinking gourd, it said.

When the song was learned
and sung all day,
Peg Leg Joe would slip away
to work for another master
and teach the song again.

One day
a slave called Molly saw her man James
sold to another master.
James would be taken away,
their family torn apart.
Just one more night together.

A quail called in the trees that night.
Molly and James remembered Joe's song.
They sang it low.

> *When the sun comes back, and the first quail calls,*
> *Follow the drinking gourd.*
> *For the old man is a-waiting for to carry you to freedom*
> *If you follow the drinking gourd.*

They looked to the sky and saw the stars.

Taking their little son Isaiah,
old Hattie, and her grandson George,
Molly and James set out for freedom
that very night,
following the stars of the drinking gourd.
They ran all night through the fields,
till they crossed the stream to the woods.

When daylight came, they hid in the trees,
watching,
listening
for the master's hounds
set loose to find them.

But the dogs lost the runaways' scent
at the stream,
and Molly and James and Isaiah,
old Hattie and young George,
were not found.
They hid all day in the woods.

At night they walked again,
singing Joe's song
and looking for the signs
that marked the trail.

The riverbank makes a very good road,
The dead trees will show you the way.
Left foot, peg foot, traveling on,
Follow the drinking gourd.

Walking by night, sleeping by day,
for weeks they traveled on.
Sometimes berries to pick
and corn to snatch,
sometimes fish to catch,
sometimes empty bellies to sleep on.
Sometimes no stars to guide the way.

They never knew what lay ahead.
There was danger from men
who would send them back,
and danger from hungry beasts.
But sometimes a kind deed was done.

One day as they hid in a thicket
a boy from a farm found them.
In a bag of feed for the hogs in the wood
he brought bacon and corn bread to share.

Singing low, they traveled on.

The river ends between two hills,
Follow the drinking gourd.
There's another river on the other side,
Follow the drinking gourd.

On and on they followed the trail
to the river's end.
From the top of the hill they saw the new path,
another river beneath the stars
to lead them to freedom land.

The drinking gourd led them on.
The song was almost done.

When the great big river meets the little river,
Follow the drinking gourd.
For the old man is a-waiting for to carry you to freedom
If you follow the drinking gourd.

Then they climbed the last hill.
Down below was Peg Leg Joe
waiting at the wide Ohio River
to carry them across.
Their spirits rose when they saw the old man.
Molly and James and Isaiah, old Hattie and George,
ran to the shore.

Under a starry sky
Joe rowed them across the wide Ohio River.
He told them of hiding places
where they would be safe.
A path of houses stretched like a train
on a secret track leading north to Canada.
He called it the Underground Railroad.
It carried riders to freedom.

The first safe house stood on the hill.
The lamp was lit,
which meant it was safe to come.
Ragged and weary, they waited
while Joe signaled low, with a hoot like an owl.
Then the door opened wide
to welcome the freedom travelers.

They were rushed through the house
to the barn,
for the farmers knew
there were slave catchers near.
A trapdoor in the floor
took them under the barn,
to hide till it was safe to move on.
Then Peg Leg Joe went back to the river
to meet others who followed the drinking gourd.

With danger still near, too close for ease,
the farmer sent the five travelers on.
He drew a map that showed the way north
on the midnight road
to the next safe house, just over two hills.

This time James called the signal,
a hoot like an owl,
that opened the door to a Quaker farm.
The travelers were led to a secret room
hidden behind shelves.

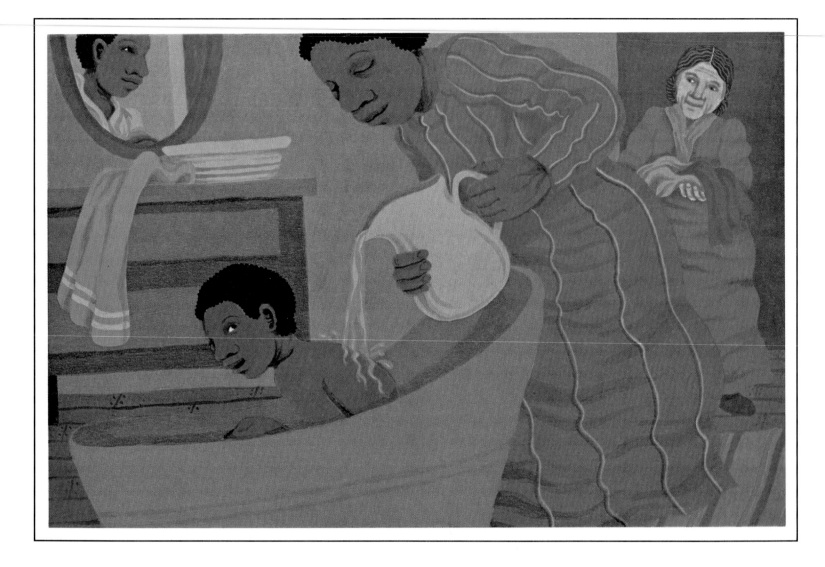

They rested here for many days
and healed their wounds.
Soft beds, full meals, new clothes, hot baths,
washed away some fear and pain.
Isaiah smiled.

When they were strong, they traveled again
from house to house on the underground trail,
still following the drinking gourd north.
Sometimes they traveled on foot,
sometimes by cart.
The wagon they rode near their journey's end
carried fruit to market
and the runaways to freedom.

At last they came to the shores of Lake Erie.
Molly and James and Isaiah,
old Hattie and young George,
climbed aboard the steamship
that would carry them across
to Canada, to freedom.
"Five more souls are safe!"
old Hattie cried.
The sun shone bright when they stepped on land.

They had followed the drinking gourd.

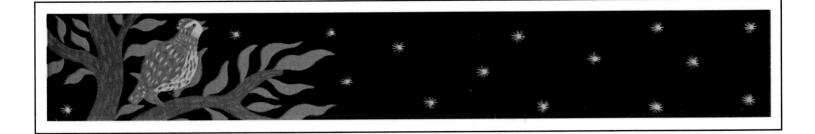

CHORUS

Fol - low _____ the drink - ing gourd! Fol - low _____ the drink - ing gourd. _ For the old man is a - wait - ing for to car - ry you to free-dom If you fol-low the drink - ing gourd. When the sun comes back, and the first quail calls, _ Fol - low _____ the drink - ing gourd. _ For the old man is a - wait - ing for to car - ry you to free-dom If you fol-low the drink - ing gourd.

VERSE

The Underground Railroad

by Glennette Turner
illustrated by Jerry Pinkney

Long ago, African people were brought to this country as slaves. Many Americans believed that slavery was wrong. Some worked secretly to help slaves escape.

This was happening at a time when railroads were being built all over the country. So the people helping the slaves used railroad words as code words. They called the secret escape paths the Underground Railroad. The escaping slaves were called passengers. The brave people who helped them were called conductors.

Harriet Tubman was a slave who escaped from Maryland and went north. She made 19 trips back into the slave states to rescue her family and many other people. She became one of the most famous conductors on the Underground Railroad.

PACIFIC
OCEAN

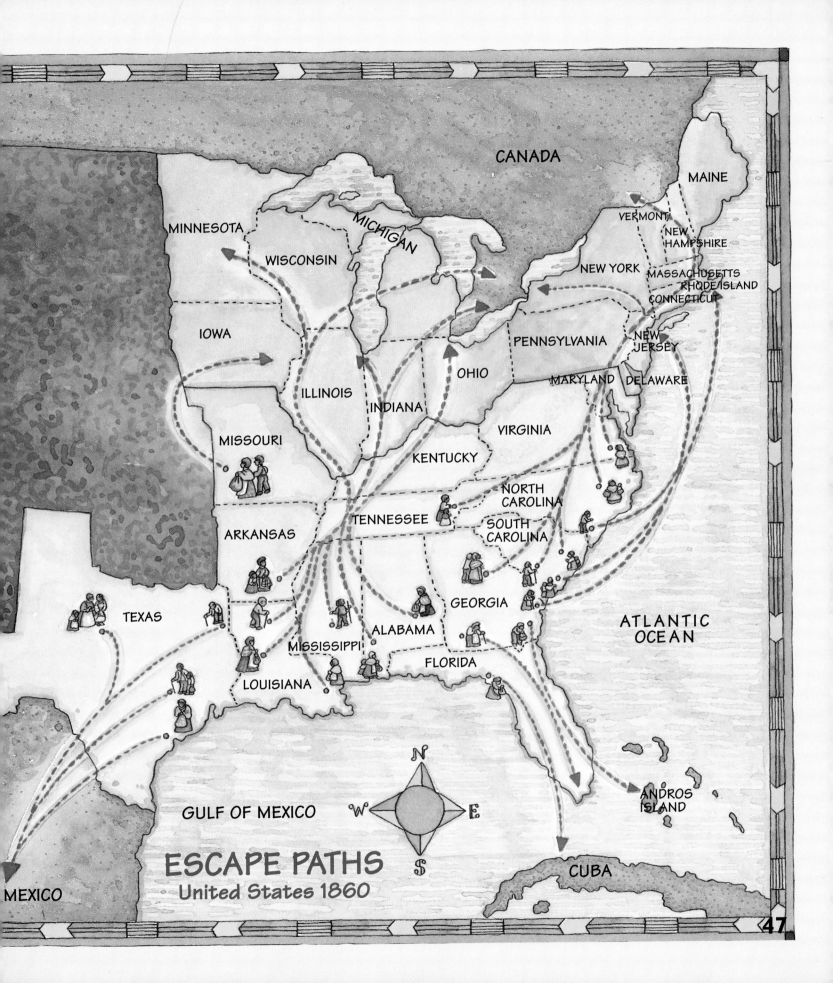

CANADA

MAINE

MINNESOTA

MICHIGAN

VERMONT

WISCONSIN

NEW
HAMPSHIRE

NEW YORK

MASSACHUSETTS

RHODE ISLAND

IOWA

CONNECTICUT

NEW
JERSEY

PENNSYLVANIA

DELAWARE

MARYLAND

ILLINOIS

OHIO

MISSOURI

INDIANA

VIRGINIA

KENTUCKY

NORTH
CAROLINA

ARKANSAS

TENNESSEE

SOUTH
CAROLINA

ATLANTIC
OCEAN

TEXAS

GEORGIA

MISSISSIPPI

ALABAMA

LOUISIANA

FLORIDA

ANDROS
ISLAND

N

GULF OF MEXICO

W   E

ESCAPE PATHS

S

United States 1860

CUBA

MEXICO

FIRE STATION

All in a Day's Work

We celebrate people who make their communities better.

Watch a subway engineer get other workers to their jobs. Then find your way through Boston.

Learn how fire fighters get their job done.

Meet a woman in charge of keeping her community safe.

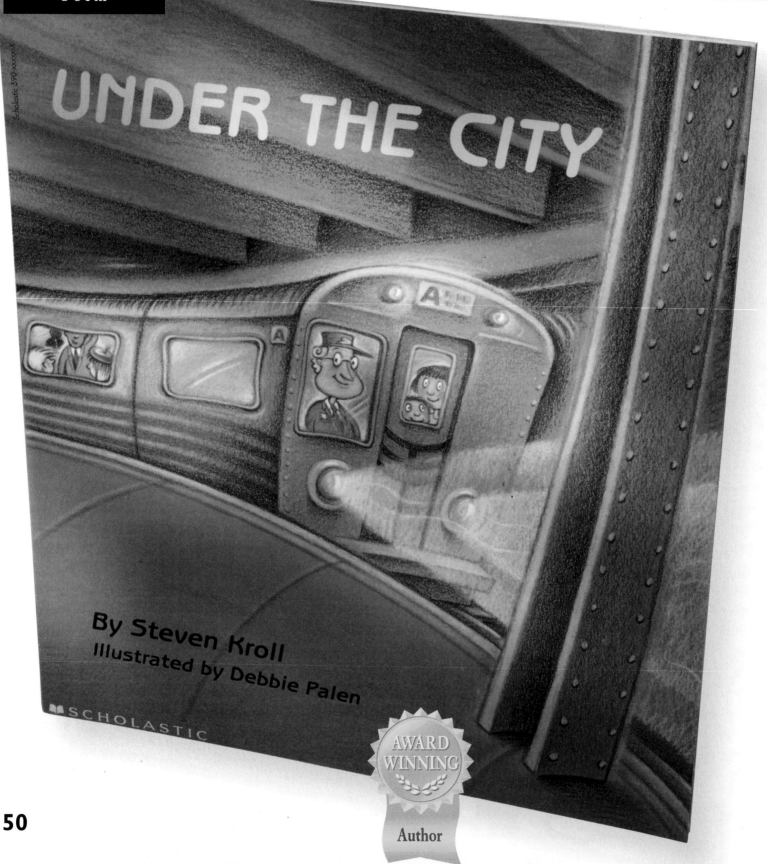

UNDER THE CITY

By Steven Kroll
Illustrated by Debbie Palen

SCHOLASTIC

AWARD
WINNING

Author

The subway engineer drives the train
Under the ground and out of the rain.
He keeps on driving, he's seldom late,
Helping his passengers keep their dates.

The subway engineer scans the track.
He knows what's ahead and what's in back.
When all the people are safely in,
He shuts the doors and the ride begins.

He drives through the tunnels out of sight.
He drives to the stations where it's light.

He picks up the plumber with her case.
She checks her watch, a smile on her face.
She'll glide to her station in a wink.
Then she'll be able to fix that sink.

He picks up the pizza man, out of luck,
Bound for help because he got stuck.
Two flat tires on a big old van,
Engineer takes him fast as he can.

He drives through the tunnels out of sight.
He drives to the stations where it's light.

The engineer picks up Roz and Tim.
He picks up their teacher Mr. Kim.
He picks up Luis, he picks up Sue.
A postal worker gets on, too.

Teacher and students sit in a row,
Balancing instruments as they go.
They'll be playing at the Westside Fair.
The subway engineer takes them there.

He drives through the tunnels out of sight.
He drives to the stations where it's light.

He picks up a nurse in uniform,
A college student bound for her dorm,
A florist holding a big bouquet,
An actor learning lines for a play.

Girls in sneakers and boys in shorts,
Heading for any of many courts.
At times it's crowded, at times it's not,
Sometimes you don't get to move a lot.

He drives through the tunnels out of sight.
He drives to the stations where it's light.

The postal worker is really beat
After a long hard day on his feet.
His feet are aching, the job is done,
The subway whisks him home to his son.

Happy tourists from many lands
Ride the train with their maps in hand.
They take in every sight and sound
As the engineer makes his round.

He drives through the tunnels out of sight.
He drives to the stations where it's light.

He drives in the summer when it's hot.
He drives in the winter when it's not.
Driving on through all kinds of weather…

The subway engineer links us together.

Under Boston

A map can help you know how to use the subway.
Look at all the different stations in Boston.

ORANGE LINE

BLUE LINE

RED LINE

GREEN LINE

ALEWIFE ♿

DAVIS ♿

PORTER ♿

LECHMERE ◇

HARVARD ♿

SCIENCE PARK

CENTRAL ♿

NORTH STATION ═

KENDALL ♿

HAYMARKET ═

BOWDOIN ◇

CHARLES/MGH

GOVERNMENT CTR

PARK STREET ♿

BOYLSTON

ARLINGTON

COPLEY

HYNES CONVENTION CENTER/ICA

KENMORE

BOSTON UNIVERSITY

BOSTON COLLEGE [B]

PRUDENTIAL

CLEVELAND CIRCLE [C]

SYMPHONY

LONGWOOD AVE

NORTHEASTERN

RIVERSIDE [D]   RESERVOIR

MUSEUM

BRIGHAM CIRCLE

HEATH

ARBORWAY [E]

♿ **OAK GROVE**

MALDEN CENTER

♿ WELLINGTON

♿ SULLIVAN SQUARE

COMMUNITY COLLEGE

STATE

DOWNTOWN CROSSING

♿ CHINATOWN

♿ NE MEDICAL CTR

♿ BACK BAY/SOUTH END

♿ MASSACHUSETTS AVE

♿ RUGGLES

♿ ROXBURY CROSSING

♿ JACKSON SQUARE

♿ STONY BROOK

♿ GREEN STREET

♿ **FOREST HILLS**

♿ **WONDERLAND**

REVERE BEACH ♿

BEACHMONT ♿

SUFFOLK DOWNS ♿

ORIENT HEIGHTS ♿

WOOD ISLAND

AIRPORT ✈

MAVERICK

AQUARIUM

♿ SOUTH STATION

♿ BROADWAY

♿ ANDREW

♿ JFK/UMASS

SAVIN HILL

FIELDS CORNER

SHAWMUT

♿ **ASHMONT**

NORTH QUINCY

WOLLASTON

♿ QUINCY CENTER

♿ QUINCY ADAMS

♿ **BRAINTREE**

MATTAPAN

WHEELCHAIR ACCESSIBLE ♿

WHEELCHAIR ACCESSIBLE
BEING CONSTRUCTED ♿

65

Fire Fighters

By Robert Maass

AWARD WINNING
Author

SCHOLASTIC

What do fire fighters do?

They have many different jobs. Their most important job is fighting fires to save lives and property. They learn this job by going to school. They are taught by experienced fire fighters.

To be a fire fighter, one of the first things to learn is how to use ladders for climbing.

Fire fighters also learn how to use ropes. They use ropes the way mountain climbers do. With a rope, fire fighters can lower themselves down a wall.

Fire fighters in training learn all about the hoses they use to fight fires. They must practice the correct way to aim the nozzle. A fire hose shoots out water with great force. It takes skill to make sure the water goes where it is supposed to go.

The hoses are attached to fire hydrants and then to the *pumper truck*. The pumper truck pumps the water from the hydrants into the hoses the fire fighters use. These hoses are called *lines*. Controlling the amount of water that comes out of the lines is an important job. Fire fighters must learn to read the gauges on the pumper truck to know when to pump more or less water into the lines. It is a job that takes lots of practice.

There are many special tools the fire fighters must learn to use. One of these tools is called the "jaws of life." It is a very powerful tool that can cut through metal. It can also be used to pry things open. When people are stuck in cars or buildings, this tool can help get them out.

There are also simple tools a fire fighter needs. One of the most important is an ax. Fire fighters often need it to break through walls, ceilings, doors, and windows during a fire.

All fire fighters wear heavy coats and gloves when fighting fires. They also wear an unusual leather helmet. It protects them from water and from things that might fall from burning buildings.

A flashlight and a doorstop come in very handy, too. They are used so often that fire fighters sometimes carry them on their helmets.

Fire fighters also wear special gear. They need to wear walkie-talkies to stay in touch with one another. They wear heat-resistant clothing because the fire is very hot. Often a fire fighter must carry a tank of air to breathe when there is a lot of smoke.

Some fire fighters receive special training. They may be assigned to a *rescue unit.* The fire fighters in these units fight fires, but also need special skills. For example, some are trained in diving to fight ship or pier fires. Diving rescue units may also be called to help people who have boating or other water accidents.

Teamwork is a very important part of learning to be a fire fighter. Everyone must work together to save lives and put out fires. Fire fighters at school march together to practice being part of a team.

After several weeks the fire fighters' basic training is over. All fire fighters must pass a test on what they have learned. Then the fire fighters graduate.

The new graduates are assigned to work with experienced fire fighters at a fire station.

Here they will put their training into practice, and learn even more from the experienced fire fighters. There are many more jobs to learn at the fire station.

All of the equipment the fire fighters use must be kept in top shape. This means that repairs must be done as soon as anything goes wrong. New fire fighters learn to maintain and repair their equipment. Tools and trucks are checked and serviced every day, because everything must work perfectly when a fire or other emergency happens.

Fire fighters must also learn to check things outside of the fire station. They check all of the fire hydrants in the neighborhoods they serve, and inspect buildings for fire safety.

There are lots of other jobs around the fire station.

Fires can break out at any time, so fire fighters in many places must be at the fire station every day and every night. That means that the fire fighters on duty must cook their own meals.

When they go shopping for groceries, they must all go together. They take their walkie-talkies to keep in touch. If a fire starts somewhere, the fire fighters will have to leave the grocery store in a hurry.

There are often visitors at the fire station. School children sometimes come to learn about fire fighting and fire prevention.

When children can't come to the fire station, fire fighters visit schools. They talk to classes about fire prevention, and what to do in case of fire.

Fire fighters demonstrate how to *stop-drop-and-roll*. This is what you must do if your clothes catch on fire. **Stop:** Stop where you are. Don't run. **Drop:** Drop to the ground. **Roll:** Roll back and forth protecting your face with your hands to smother the flames.

When all of the work has been done at the fire station, there are other things to do. Some fire fighters may get a chance to read the paper. Some may exercise in order to keep in shape. There may be a dog to take care of, too.

Occasionally, fire fighters may even try to sleep. But no matter what fire fighters may be doing, they must always be ready. Because sooner or later, usually when no one is expecting it...the alarm will ring.

As soon as the alarm goes off, the fire fighters must put on their fire-fighting gear and get to their trucks as fast as they can. Many fire stations have poles to help fire fighters get downstairs. Poles are faster and safer than stairs. Everyone hurries. They know that the best way to control a fire is to get there as quickly as possible.

Each fire fighter has a special place on one of the trucks. As the engines pull out of the fire station, the fire fighters check the equipment they will need.

Some of the trucks need two drivers. One is in the front of the truck and one is at the back, or *tiller*. The one in the back handles the rear wheels of the longest fire trucks.

As soon as they arrive, the fire fighters jump off the trucks and go to work. Each fire fighter knows what to do.

80

A fire chief is on hand to direct the firefight.

Some of the fire fighters must *vent* the roof. That means they must break a hole in the roof to release fire and smoke trapped in the building. That will make it easier to fight the fire and rescue people inside.

Other fire fighters have attached the lines to pumper trucks. They begin to aim streams of water at the flames. Some must enter the building to fight the fire from inside.

Windows must sometimes be broken to let the smoke and heat out of the building. Fire fighters carry tanks of air on their backs so they can breathe pure air when the smoke is very thick.

The flames and smoke of the fire begin to disappear as the fire fighters gain control of it. After a while, the fire appears to be over. But the fire fighters' job is not over. They must carefully check the building to make sure that every bit of the fire is out.

Finally, the fire is completely out. Struggling to put out a fire is exhausting work. Some of the fire fighters must rest before they put their equipment back into the trucks.

The fire-fighting team packs all of its tools and gear back into the trucks. Everything will be ready when the next fire occurs. The fire trucks return to the fire station. They back in so they will be ready to roll as soon as the alarm sounds again.

The fire fighters are happy to be back at the fire station. They are tired, but they are safe.

Fire fighting is very dangerous work. Sometimes fire fighters lose their lives in fires.

But the brave men and women who have died fighting fires are not forgotten. In almost every city and town, there is a monument to remember those who gave their lives trying to save others. At least once each year, fire fighters get together to remember.

In many places fire fighters also get together to take part in special parades. Fire fighters wash and shine all of their trucks so they will look their very best on parade day. Then they get dressed in fresh uniforms.

Fire fighters love marching in parades with music and flags.

So do future fire fighters.

Nadine Jojola

Police Officer

**Do you think YOU can help the police?
You CAN—by keeping yourself safe!**

There are many kinds of workers who help people in their communities. When Nadine Jojola (ha-HOLE-ah) was a little girl, she wanted to be a teacher. Today she is a teacher, but not in a classroom.

Ms. Jojola is a police lieutenant in New Mexico. She teaches people in the pueblo of Isleta how to keep themselves safe in their community.

91

All About

Nadine Jojola

Here's how Police Lieutenant Nadine Jojola lends a hand in her community.

Lieutenant Jojola enjoys teaching people, especially children and the elderly. She tells them what is right and wrong. She says, "It's a big job to teach people about the law and how to keep their community safe."

A large river called the Rio Grande runs through the pueblo. Lieutenant Jojola teaches children how to keep themselves safe around the water. She tells them not to play in the river unless an adult is with them.

Lieutenant Jojola warns children about other dangers. She tells them never to go off with a stranger. She tells them how they can know if something is poison. She tells them they should never play with matches. She teaches children how to dial 911 in an emergency.

And, of course, she tells them that the police will always help with serious problems.

Nadine Jojola's
Tips for Helping Police

1 If you see trouble, tell an adult what is wrong.

2 Learn about what can hurt you and how to keep yourself safe.

3 Ask the police for help with serious problems.

93

Small Ways

The little things we do can make a big difference.

A grandmother's gentle ways and special food add a wonderful touch to a class's day.

See how one boy gives a new look to a whole village. Then meet a girl whose community has a long tradition of doing the same thing.

AWARD WINNING Book

Halmoni and the Picnic

Sook Nyul Choi

Illustrated by **Karen M. Dugan**

Hand in hand, Yunmi and her grandmother, Halmoni, walked toward St. Patrick's Elementary School. Taxi cabs darted between the big buses rumbling down busy Fourteenth Street. Yunmi squeezed Halmoni's hand and smiled. Halmoni nodded in acknowledgment, but kept her eyes on the street without smiling. Just like the day before, Halmoni looked sad as they drew closer to the school. She did not like going back to their empty apartment all alone.

Miss Stein, in her white uniform, was coming back from working the night shift at Beth Israel Hospital.

"Good morning, Miss Stein!" Yunmi called.

"Oh, hello, Yunmi," said Miss Stein, half smiling and half yawning.

"Yunmi," Halmoni said in Korean, "you must not call out to grown-ups. You should lower your eyes out of respect. It is rude for little ones to disturb their elders!"

Yunmi giggled. "Halmoni, people like it when I greet them. In America it isn't rude to call grown-ups by their names. Here it is rude *not* to say hello and *not* to look people in the eye when you speak to them."

Halmoni sighed. "I will never get used to living here."

Yunmi was sad for her grandmother, who found America too different from Korea.

"Halmoni," she said, "my friends like the bags of fruit you give them each morning."

"I am glad. It is always nice to share with friends," said Halmoni.

"Will you please say hello to my friends in English this morning? They will be so surprised to hear you talk to them. I know you can. Please, Halmoni?"

Halmoni replied, "No, I have only been here for two months. English words are still too difficult for my old tongue. I will sound funny. I will give them this fruit; that is my way of saying hello to them. Besides, you do enough talking for both of us!"

"Yunmi, Yunmi, wait for me!" they heard Anna Marie shout from behind them.

Then Helen came running up from a side street. "Hi, Anna Marie! Hi, Yunmi!"

They said hello to Halmoni. Halmoni nodded and gave one brown bag to each girl.

"Oh, thank you!" said Helen.

"Goody," said Anna Marie. "An apple, grapes, and cherries, too!" The girls said goodbye to Halmoni and headed toward the school yard.

Helen said, "Yunmi, your grandmother is so nice, but she never says anything. Why don't you teach her some English?"

Yunmi shook her head sadly. "My grandmother is embarrassed to speak with an accent. She could speak English if she wanted to. She is smart. She used to be a teacher in Korea."

Helen thought for a while. "Maybe your grandmother is not happy here. When I'm not happy, I don't want to learn anything new. Maybe she's like me."

"That's true. I'm like that, too," Anna Marie agreed.

Yunmi sighed just like Halmoni and said, "I think she's lonely when I'm at school. My parents are so busy working that they have no time for her. I know she misses her old friends, but I don't want her to go back to Korea."

"She needs new friends!" Anna Marie exclaimed. "We can be her friends. We see her every day and we like her."

"We must do something to show her that we want to be her new friends," Helen said with determination. "What can we do?"

They entered the school yard and sat under the big oak tree thinking quietly. That morning they did not play tag or jump rope. When the bell rang, they went to their classroom and unpacked their bookbags in silence.

"Children, I have a special announcement to make this morning," Mrs. Nolan said. "Next Tuesday is our annual picnic in Central Park. We need a chaperon, so please ask your parents if one of them can come and help us."

Helen and Anna Marie raised their arms high, nearly falling off their chairs. Surprised, Mrs. Nolan said, "Yes, Helen, you first. What is it?"

Helen blushed, then asked, "Can Yunmi's grandmother be our chaperon, please?"

Mrs. Nolan said, "Of course. But Yunmi must ask her grandmother first. Will you, Yunmi?"

Helen and Anna Marie grinned and nodded at Yunmi with excitement. But Yunmi was suddenly confused and worried. What if Halmoni did not want to come? What if the children made fun of her pointed rubber shoes and her long Korean dress?

That afternoon Yunmi cautiously told Halmoni what had happened at school.

Halmoni blushed with pleasure. "Helen said that? Your teacher wants me?"

So relieved to see Halmoni looking happy, Yunmi nodded her head up and down.

Touching Yunmi's cheek, Halmoni asked, "And do you want me to go to the picnic with you?"

"Yes, yes, Halmoni, it will be fun. You will meet all my friends, and Mrs. Nolan, and we will be together all day long in Central Park."

"Then yes, I will come," Halmoni said.

Halmoni would not go to the picnic empty-handed. She prepared a huge fruit basket for the third graders. She also insisted on making large plates of kimbap and a big jug of barley tea. Kimbap is made of rice, carrots, eggs, and green vegetables wrapped in seaweed. Again, Yunmi was worried. Most of the children would bring bologna or peanut butter sandwiches, which they would wash down with soda pop. What if no one wanted to eat Halmoni's kimbap? What if they made faces?

"Halmoni, please do not take the kimbap to the picnic. It took you so long to make. Let's save it for us to eat later."

"Oh, it was no problem. It looks so pretty and it's perfect for picnics. I wonder if I made enough."

On the morning of the picnic, Yunmi and her grandmother met the bus at school. Halmoni wore her pale blue skirt and top, called a ch'ima and chogori in Korean, with her white socks and white pointed rubber shoes.

When they arrived at Central Park, Halmoni sat under a big chestnut tree and watched the children play. The children took off their jackets and threw them in front of Halmoni. Smiling, she picked them up, shook off the grass and dirt, and folded each of them neatly. She liked the cool earth beneath her and the ringing laughter of the children.

After lunch, some children asked Halmoni to hold one end of their jump rope. Others asked if Halmoni would make kimbap again for next year's picnic. When Yunmi translated, Halmoni nodded and said, "Kurae, kurae," meaning "Yes, yes."

The children started to chant as they jumped rope:

"One, two, pointed shoe.
Three, four, kimbap more.
Five, six, chopsticks.
Seven, eight, kimbap plate.
Kurae, kurae, Picnic Day!"

Halmoni smiled until tears clouded her vision. Her long blue ch'ima danced in the breeze as she turned the jump rope. She tapped her shoes to the rhythm of their song.

Mrs. Nolan asked Yunmi, "What should the class call your grandmother? Mrs. Lee?"

Yunmi said, "I just call her Halmoni, which means grandmother. In Korea, it is rude to call elders by their names."

Mrs. Nolan nodded and smiled. "Children, why don't we all thank Halmoni for her delicious kimbap?"

"Thank you for the kimbap, Halmoni!" the children shouted in unison. Halmoni's wrinkled face turned red and she looked down at her pointed shoes. She took a handkerchief from the large sleeve of her chogori and wiped her eyes.

Halmoni was deep in thought as the big bus wove through the New York City streets. When the bus arrived back at school, the children hurried off, shouting goodbye. Halmoni murmured in English, "Goodbye, goodbye."

Filled with pride, Yunmi grabbed Halmoni's hand and gave it a squeeze. Halmoni squeezed back. Yunmi grinned, thinking of Halmoni's big smile as the children sang about her in Central Park. Skipping along Fourteenth Street, Yunmi hummed the kimbap song.

She thought she heard Halmoni quietly humming along, too.

The Little Painter of Sabana Grande

by Patricia Maloney Markun · illustrated by Robert Casilla

AWARD
WINNING

Book

High in the mountains of Panama lies the village of Sabana Grande. It is very small. Just seven houses of clay adobe stand alongside a brook in a grassy meadow. In the middle house lives the Espino family.

At dawn one cool purple morning, the rooster next door crowed. The Espinos woke up.

Papa went off to the meadow to milk the cow.

Mama stirred up the fire in the open-air kitchen and fried golden breakfast tortillas.

Fernando rolled up his straw sleeping mat and put it in the corner. He hurried to the kitchen to eat his tortilla right away.

This was an important day. At school Fernando had learned to draw colored pictures with crayons. Now school was out for dry-season vacation, and Fernando was going to paint for the first time.

His teacher, Señora Arias, had told him exactly how the country people of Panama made their paints. She said:

"Black from the charcoal of a burned tree stump.
Blue of certain berries that grow deep in the jungle.
Yellow from dried grasses in the meadow.
And red from the clay on the bottom of the brook."

It took him a long time to make the paints. Black was easy, because the burned stump of a big tree lay right next to the Espinos' adobe house.

But Fernando had to look before he found those certain berries deep in the jungle, to make the blue paint.

In the corner of the meadow he found a patch of very dry grass, and from that he made a large pot of yellow.

He wandered up and down alongside the brook, looking for clay. The fast-flowing water was too deep for him to reach down to the bottom. At last he came to a bend in the brook where the water was shallow. He reached down and dug up a fistful of clay. It was red, just the way Señora Arias had said.

Now his paints were stirred up and waiting—black, blue, yellow, and red, in four bowls. Next he got out the three paintbrushes his teacher had given him—one very small, one medium-sized, and one especially large.

I'm ready to paint pictures, Fernando said to himself. He picked up the small brush and dipped it into the pot of red. Then he had a terrible thought.

He had nothing to paint a picture on! An artist needs paper.

He looked in both rooms of the house. He could find no paper at all.

He ran from house to house asking everyone in Sabana Grande for paper to paint on. None of the neighbors had any. Not a scrap.

Fernando was sad. After all his work he wouldn't be able to paint pictures—the colored pictures he could almost see, he wanted to make them so badly. Paints and brushes weren't enough. He needed paper, too.

His fingers itched to draw something—anything. He put down the paintbrush and went over to the mud by the brook. He picked up a stick and drew in the wet dirt, the way he had ever since he was a very little boy.

The big rooster who woke him every morning came out of the chicken yard next door. Fernando looked at him and drew the shape of a rooster. He sighed. He couldn't use his new red and yellow paints to make a bright rooster. He couldn't make the rooster's comb red. He could only scratch out a mud-colored rooster. It wasn't the same as painting would be. It didn't have any color.

Fernando looked around at the adobe houses of his village. Suddenly he got an idea. Adobe was smooth and white— almost like paper. Why couldn't he paint on the outside of his family's adobe house?

"No!" Papa said. "Who ever saw pictures on the outside of a house?"

"No!" Mama agreed. "What would the neighbors say?"

Fernando looked at his pots of paint and was very unhappy. He wanted to paint pictures more than anything else he could think of.

At last Papa said, "I can't stand to see my boy so miserable. All right, Fernando. Go ahead and paint on the house!"

Mama said, "Do your best, Fernando. Remember, the neighbors will have to look at your pictures for a very long time."

First Fernando made a tiny plan of the pictures he was going to paint, painting it with his smallest brush on one corner of the house.

"Your plan looks good to me, Fernando," Papa said. "If you can paint pictures small, you should be able to paint them big."

Fernando picked up his bigger brushes and started to paint a huge picture of the most beautiful tree in Panama, the flowering poinciana, on the left side of the front door. As he painted, he could look up and see the red flowers of a poinciana tree, just beginning its dry season, blooming on the mountainside.

The neighbors were very surprised.

Señora Endara called out, "Come and see what Fernando is doing!"

Señor Remon said, "Who ever saw a house with pictures on the outside?"

Pepita, the little girl next door, asked, "Does your mother know you're painting on your house?"

Fernando nodded and smiled and kept on painting. Now and then he would look up at the mountain to see the real poinciana. After a week its flowers faded and died. Fernando's tree grew bigger and brighter and redder.

On one branch he added a black toucan with a flat, yellow bill. On another branch a lazy, brown sloth hung by its three toes.

The neighbors brought out chairs. While Fernando worked, they drank coffee and watched him paint.

Next he painted the wall on the other side of the door. An imaginary vine with flat, green leaves and huge, purple blossoms crept up the wall.

Word spread about the little painter of Sabana Grande. Even people from Santa Marta, the village around the mountain, hiked into town to watch him paint. The purple vine now reached almost to the thatched roof.

One day Señora Arias came from the school in Santa Marta. Why was his teacher looking for him, Fernando wondered. It was still dry season, when there wasn't any school. It hadn't rained for a month.

"School's not starting yet," his teacher said. "I came to see your painted adobe house that everyone in Santa Marta is talking about. Fernando, you did very well with those paintbrushes. I like it!"

She turned to the neighbors. "Don't you?"

"We certainly do!" the neighbors agreed.

They poured some coffee for the visiting teacher.

"Fernando, will you paint pictures on my house?" asked Señora Alfaro.

"And mine, too?" asked Señor Remon.

Fernando nodded yes, but he kept on painting.

For fun he added a black, white-faced monkey looking down at the people through purple flowers.

Next to the door he painted a big red-and-yellow rooster, flopping its red comb as it crowed a loud "cock-a-doodle-doo!"

145

Above the door he painted the words CASA FAMILIA
ESPINO, so people would know that this was the home
of the Espino family.

Now his pictures were finished. Fernando sat down with his teacher and the neighbors. Everyone said kind words about his paintings.

Fernando said nothing. He just smiled and thought to himself, There are still six adobe houses left to paint in Sabana Grande.

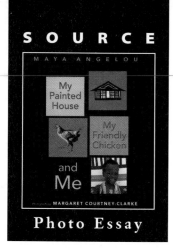

SOURCE

Photo Essay

from My Painted House, My Friendly Chicken, and Me

by Maya Angelou
photographs by Margaret Courtney-Clarke

Hello Stranger-friend.

I am Thandi, an Ndebele girl in South Africa.

All Ndebele women paint their houses, and I want you to know, stranger-friend, no one's house is as good as my mother's. She has started to teach me to paint good, very good designs.

When I am
taller, I shall
have a house so
good people
will stop in
front of my
walls and smile,
and even laugh
out loud.

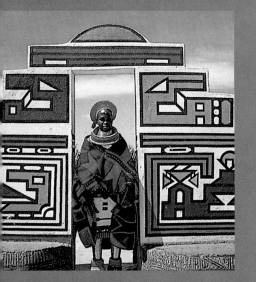

You have to have strong eyes to paint good, and your hand must not shake like a leaf on a tree, for you must fill a chicken's feather with paint and draw a line as straight as a spear.

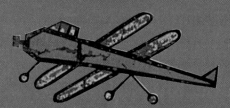

You must have the

pattern inside your head,

even before you dip the

feather into the paint.

Your hand must be

steady to make the

patterns sharp,

and your legs must be strong, because sometimes the walls are high.

Glossary

blushed
became red
in the face

He always **blushed**
during show-and-tell.

cautiously
carefully, so as not
to be in danger
or get hurt

You should cross a
street **cautiously**.

charcoal
a dark material made
by burning wood

The artist drew
a picture with
charcoal.

confused
mixed up

It is easy to be
confused in a
new place.

country
a land that people
live in

The United States is
a **country** in North
America.

crayons
sticks of colored
wax used for writing
or drawing

He drew that picture
of his backyard
with **crayons**.

different
not the same

Mom likes to wear
a **different** hat
every day.

doorstop
something that
holds a door open

The **doorstop** kept
the door from
slamming shut on
a windy day.

embarrassed
uncomfortable,
ashamed

I felt **embarrassed**
when I slipped on
the ice.

engineer

a person who drives a train

The **engineer** drove the train safely.

equipment

the things a person needs to do a job

A fire fighter needs **equipment** such as hoses and ladders to put out a fire.

flashlight

a light that is small enough to carry in your hand

We used a **flashlight** to find our way home in the dark.

flashlight

free

not held back or kept in by anyone else

The people in America wanted to be **free** and rule themselves.

freedom

being able to move or act without being held back

Many slaves ran away to find **freedom**.

gear

the tools and other things a person needs to do a job or an activity

We left the tents and other camping **gear** under the big tree.

helmet

a hard hat that protects the head

She didn't hurt her head when she fell because she was wearing a **helmet**.

helmet

hounds
hunting dogs
The police used **hounds** to find the lost child.

hydrants
water pipes that stick out of the street and are used for fighting fires
The fire fighters joined their hoses to the **hydrants** to get water.

independence
freedom to rule yourself
The new country won its **independence**.

journey
a trip
We went on a **journey** to visit Aunt Joan.

paint
to make a picture with paints
I am going to **paint** a picture of my little brother.

paintbrushes
brushes used to paint a picture or cover something with paint
The artist used many **paintbrushes** to paint the picture.

paintings
pictures made with paints
My favorite **paintings** show beautiful gardens.

pictures
things you draw, paint, or take with a camera
I like to draw **pictures** of people at the beach.

scent
a smell
The **scent** of the flowers is wonderful.

painting

secretly
done in a hidden way
The people **secretly** planned to run away.

stations
places where a train stops
Many people got off the train at the two main **stations**.

subway
a train that runs under the ground
The **subway** took us from one part of the city to another part.

train
a line of cars that run on a track
We rode in the first car of the **train**.

tunnels
roads or paths under the ground or water that trains or cars can go through
The train went through two long **tunnels** on this trip.

uniforms
special clothes worn by people doing different jobs
The **uniforms** of our police officers are dark blue.

walkie-talkies
radio sets that are carried and used by people to talk to each other
The police carry **walkie-talkies** to call for help.

war
a fight between groups of people
The **war** went on for three years.

worried
afraid of bad things happening
The father is **worried** about his children playing in the street.

train

347C

Authors and Illustrators

Aliki pages 10-17

It takes a long time for Aliki to finish the nonfiction books she writes. One reason is that she spends lots of time getting information for each book. The other reason is that she not only writes the books but draws the pictures, too. Two other books by Aliki are *Communication* and *Fossils Tell of Long Ago.*

Maya Angelou pages 148-153

Maya Angelou worked at many different jobs before she became a famous writer. She cooked in restaurants and worked in a car repair shop. When she was still in high school, she was the first African-American female streetcar conductor in San Francisco. You can find more of Angelou's poems in *Soul Looks Back in Wonder.*

Robert Casilla pages 124-147

Robert Casilla has illustrated many books, but painting the pictures for *The Little Painter of Sabana Grande* was really special. He says the town where this book takes place reminded him of Puerto Rico, where he lived for a while as a child. Some other books with illustrations by Casilla are *A Picture Book of Jesse Owens* by David Adler and *Rodeo Day* by Jonelle Torisera.

Sook Nyul Choi pages 96-123

Sook Nyul Choi first came to the United States from Korea when she was a college student. Like Halmoni, the author found there were many things she missed about Korea and many things to learn about her new country. Choi worked as a teacher in New York City for 20 years. She now lives in Massachusetts and spends her time writing.

Acknowledgments

Grateful acknowledgment is made to the following sources for permission to reprint from previously published material. The publisher has made diligent efforts to trace the ownership of all copyrighted material in this volume and believes that all necessary permissions have been secured. If any errors or omissions have inadvertently been made, proper corrections will gladly be made in future editions.

Cover: Steve Schudlich.

Interior: Selection and cover from THE MANY LIVES OF BENJAMIN FRANKLIN by Aliki. Copyright © 1988 by Aliki Brandenberg. Reprinted with permission of Simon & Schuster Books for Young Readers, Simon & Schuster Children's Publishing Division.

"Follow the Drinking Gourd" from FOLLOW THE DRINKING GOURD by Jeanette Winter. Copyright © 1988 by Jeanette Winter. Reprinted by arrangement with Alfred A. Knopf, Inc.

Harriet Tubman illustration by Jerry Pinkney in "The Underground Railroad" from FROM SEA TO SHINING SEA compiled by Amy L. Cohn. Illustration copyright © 1993 by Jerry Pinkney. Published by Scholastic Inc. Used by permission.

UNDER THE CITY by Steven Kroll, illustrated by Debbie Palen. Copyright © 1996 by Scholastic Inc.

T Map of Boston Subway lines and logo are used by permission of the Massachusetts Bay Transportation Authority.

"Fire Fighters" from FIRE FIGHTERS by Robert Maass. Copyright © 1989 by Robert Maass. Reprinted by permission of Scholastic Inc.

"Halmoni and the Picnic" from HALMONI AND THE PICNIC by Sook Nyul Choi, illustrated by Karen Milone Dugan. Text copyright © 1993 by Sook Nyul Choi. Illustrations copyright © 1993 by Karen Milone Dugan. Reprinted by permission of Houghton Mifflin Company. All rights reserved.

"The Little Painter of Sabana Grande" from THE LITTLE PAINTER OF SABANA GRANDE by Patricia Maloney Markun, illustrated by Robert Casilla. Text copyright © 1993 by Patricia Maloney Markun. Illustrations copyright © 1993 by Robert Casilla. This edition is reprinted by arrangement with Simon & Schuster Books for Young Readers, Simon & Schuster Children's Publishing Division.

Selection and cover from MY PAINTED HOUSE, MY FRIENDLY CHICKEN, AND ME by Maya Angelou, photographs by Margaret Courtney-Clarke. Text copyright © 1994 by Maya Angelou. Photographs copyright © 1994 by Margaret Courtney-Clark. Reprinted by permission of Clarkson N. Potter, a division of Crown Publishers, Inc.

Cover from CAM JANSEN AND THE MYSTERY OF THE BABE RUTH BASEBALL by David A. Adler, illustrated by Susanna Natti. Illustration copyright © 1982 by Susanna Natti. Published by Viking Penguin, a division of Penguin Books USA Inc.

Cover from CAR WASHING STREET by Denise Lewis Patrick, illustrated by John Ward. Illustration copyright © 1993 by John Ward. Published by Tambourine Books, a division of William Morrow & Company, Inc.

Cover from THE CONVERSATION CLUB by Diane Stanley. Illustration copyright © 1983 by Diane Stanley Vennema. Published by Aladdin Books, Simon & Schuster Children's Publishing Division.

Cover from THE WOMAN WHO OUTSHONE THE SUN by Children's Book Press and Rosalma Zubizarreta, illustrated by Fernando Olivera. Illustration copyright © 1991 by Fernando Olivera. Published by Children's Books Press.

Photography and Illustration Credits

Selection Opener Photographs by David S. Waitz Photography/Alleycat Design, Inc.

Photos: p. 2 c, cl: © Marcia Keegan for Scholastic Inc.; tc: © John Cancalosi/DRK Photo. p. 3 br: © Marcia Keegan for Scholastic Inc.; cl: John Gerlach/DRK Photo. pp. 90-93: © Marcia Keegan for Scholastic Inc. p. 155 bl: © Richard Megna for Scholastic Inc. br: © Dick Clintsman for Scholastic Inc. p. 156 br: © Bill Losh/FPG International Corp. p. 157 bc: © Don Mason/The Stock Market. p. 158 br: © Steve Dunwell; bl: Courtesy of HarperCollins. p. 159 bl: Courtesy of Holiday House; br: Courtesy of Houghton Mifflin.

Illustrations: pp. 2-3: Jackie Snider; pp. 8-9: Steve Schudlich; pp. 10-17: Mary Keefe; pp. 46-47: John Wallner; pp. 50-64: Debbie Palen; pp. 48-49, 94-95: Steve Schudlich.